MERLIN: THE OFFICIAL ANNUAL 2012
A BANTAM BOOK 978 0 857 51000 6

First published in Great Britain by Bantam,
an imprint of Random House Children's Books
A Random House Group Company.

This edition published 2011

1 3 5 7 9 10 8 6 4 2

Bantam Books are published by Random House Children's Books,
61–63 Uxbridge Road, London W5 5SA

www.kidsatrandomhouse.co.uk
www.totallyrandombooks.co.uk
www.randomhouse.co.uk

Addresses for companies within The Random House Group Limited can be found at:
www.randomhouse.co.uk/offices.htm

THE RANDOM HOUSE GROUP Limited Reg. No. 954009

A CIP catalogue record for this book is available from the British Library.

Printed in Italy

CONTENTS

MERLIN

As magic continues to be outlawed in the
kingdom of Camelot, this young warlock is
still forced to hide his powers. His destiny
is slowly unveiling as Merlin saves Prince
Arthur's life time and time again. His sense
of what is right and just keeps him loyal
to the use of magic for good and for
what he believes is its true purpose –
making sure Arthur becomes
the Once and Future King.

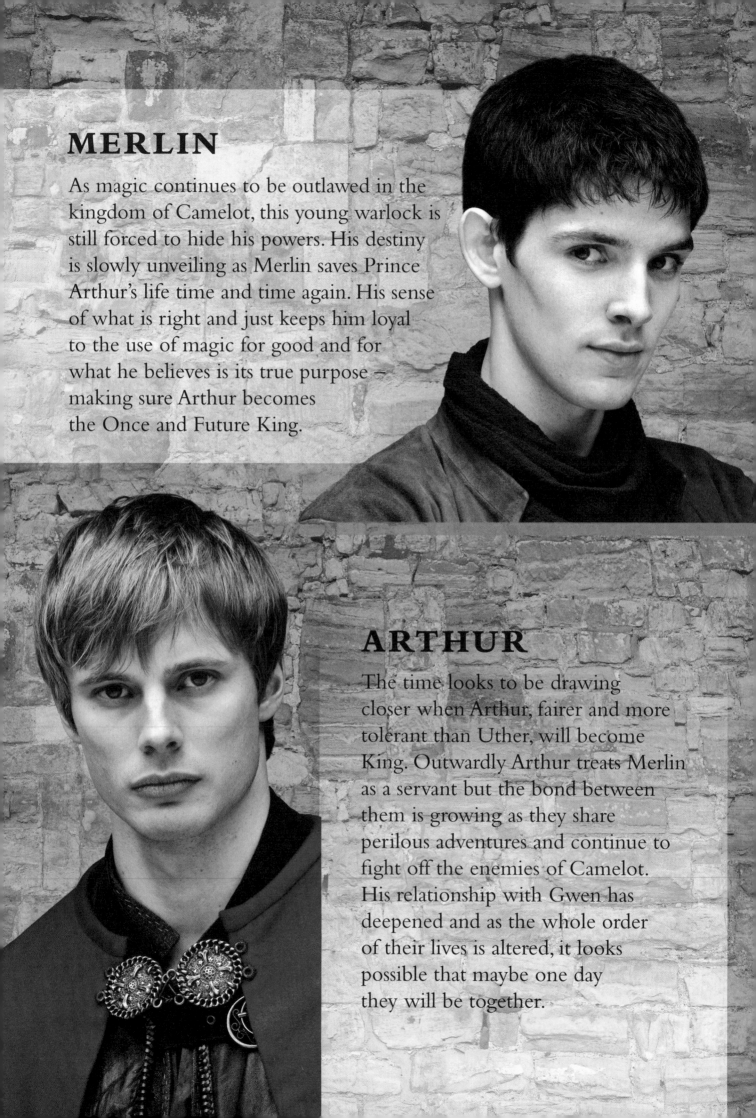

ARTHUR

The time looks to be drawing
closer when Arthur, fairer and more
tolerant than Uther, will become
King. Outwardly Arthur treats Merlin
as a servant but the bond between
them is growing as they share
perilous adventures and continue to
fight off the enemies of Camelot.
His relationship with Gwen has
deepened and as the whole order
of their lives is altered, it looks
possible that maybe one day
they will be together.

MORGANA

Having found her half-sister Morgause and discovered that Uther is her father, Morgana is in turmoil. Her practice of dark magic has increased and she will stop at nothing to avenge the wrongs she believes have afflicted her. She no longer feels loyalty to anyone in Camelot. Merlin knows she is no longer the dutiful ward of the King but feels powerless to expose her.

GWEN

Guinevere is still fiercely loyal to those around her but she is becoming increasingly distrustful of her mistress, Morgana. As her relationship with Arthur deepens, she dares to allow herself to hope that one day they can be together without having to keep their feelings a secret. When Arthur shows her how much he cares for her by rescuing her brother and risking his own life, she is everlastingly grateful.

CAMELOT CHARACTERS

Can you solve these clues and complete
the crossword without help?

DOWN

1. Gaius' love returns but she isn't quite what she seems (5)
2. He fights better than most knights but is banned from Camelot by Uther (6)
3. The Once and Future King (6)
4. The current king of Camelot (5)
6. A proposed bride for Arthur turns out to have a Sidhe inside her (5)
8. He has to keep his magic secret and use his powers for good to protect Arthur (6)
9. He is anxious to become a knight and used to have feelings for Gwen (8)
11. Merlin's old magic name (5)
13. Morgana's half sister (8)

ACROSS

2. This boy used magic for the wrong reasons, so he could win in the tournament (5)
5. Merlin sees her in the Avalon water when he needs help (5)
7. This knight escapes from Camelot dressed up in women's clothes! (4)
10. This dastardly rival king will stop at nothing to claim the lands of Camelot (6)
12. The King's ward (7)
14. Uther and Arthur's surname (9)
16. The King's physician (5)

DEADLY DISGUISE!

It's a busy day in Camelot and someone in disguise
has managed to blend in with the crowd.
Can you spot the villain in the scene?

GOBLIN'S GOLD

The library of Camelot was a dusty and chaotic place. Merlin had been sent by Gaius to fetch an important book he wanted. As Merlin searched up and down the old shelves, he spied it just out of reach. He stretched to grab it. Suddenly the whole bookcase spun around, taking a startled Merlin with it and revealing a secret chamber!

Books, boxes and strange fantastical objects lay strewn about the room, covered in dust and cobwebs. As Merlin picked his way through the debris, he knocked against an octagonal shaped chest. Muffled growling and knocking noises seemed to be coming from inside it!

Hidden away from prying eyes, Merlin used a magic spell to untie the old leather strap that was keeping the chest closed. As the chest opened, a small leaf-green man with pointed ears popped out, like a jack-in-the-box. He had intricate tattoos on his body and large gold earrings – what a strange sight! "Boo!" he shouted at the startled warlock.

The mischievous little green man started to throw things at Merlin. Books and ancient valuable objects were flying everywhere! As he reached for a large vase, Merlin pleaded with him, "No, no!" but he ignored him and sent the vase crashing to the floor.

The little man had been squashed and squished inside the box for more than fifty years, but Merlin had grown tired of his games. "You're going back in the box until I figure out what to do with you," he told him. The little fellow played along and padded back towards the box he came from. At the last moment, he sprung onto the lid of the box and vaulted onto Merlin's head …"Ha Ha, fooled you!" …Merlin grabbed a rug from the floor and used it as a net to ensnare the creature. After a struggle, the little man suddenly disappeared into thin air!

A spot of light started to buzz around the room. It was the little green man! Merlin watched with growing horror as the little man darted out of the secret room and started to kick books off the shelves in the main library.

Careful not to leave the book he had found for Gaius, Merlin followed the trail of destruction to Arthur's chambers. Under Arthur's bed, the little green man could be heard. "Not here," he was saying disappointedly. "None here, either." Arthur's chambers were getting very untidy with clothes, bedding and crockery strewn everywhere. Arthur appeared at the entrance to his room and was shocked to find it in such a state.

"I really hope you have a good explanation for this!" said Arthur in disbelief. Merlin pretended he was spring cleaning …

Next, the speedy little man made it into Morgana's chambers, where he seemed to find things more to his liking. He went through Morgana's jewellery, discarding most of it but picking up her healing bracelet of silver and gold. As Merlin caught up with him, he jumped out of the window, knocking all the jewellery on the floor. Merlin quickly closed the window and locked it.

Back at Gaius' chambers, Merlin told Gaius all about the strange
little man and they consulted a book together to try and find
out what it was. "That's it!" said Merlin pointing to a
creature in the book. "It seems you've unleashed
a goblin," Gaius replied. "Goblins are the most
mischievous of creatures . . . and dangerous.
They will stop at nothing until they get
their hands on the one thing they value
above all others . . . gold!"

Just then there was a tap at the door and
Arthur entered. He needed Gaius on a
matter of "extreme urgency and delicacy".
He led them to Uther's chambers, where
Uther was looking extremely angry –
he'd gone completely bald! Gaius knew
that only an enchantment could cause
such an ailment and had no doubt that
the Goblin was to blame!

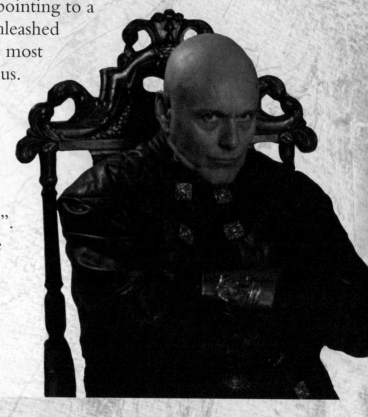

On the way back to the apothecary, Merlin
couldn't help smiling at the memory of Uther's
bald head, but Gaius soon pulled him up.
"What do you think Uther will do to the
person who released this goblin?" he asked.
"How do we catch it?" Merlin asked, as
he realized that they needed to get rid of
the goblin and quickly, before it caused
more chaos.

Gaius and Merlin agreed that a gold trap
was the best way to catch the goblin, but
getting a lot of gold wasn't an easy task!
Thankfully, Merlin knew that Prince
Arthur had a chest full of gold under
his bed, which the goblin hadn't
found in his search. Later that night,
while Arthur was sleeping, Merlin
crept into his chambers and pulled
out the chest.

Gaius and Merlin laid out a gold coin trail leading to the chest. When the goblin appeared, the door closed behind it and Merlin threw a sack over it. Again the naughty goblin quickly changed to a spot of bright light and as Merlin dived after it, he missed and fell to the floor.

While Merlin was face down on the floor, the light shot straight into Gaius's ear. "You let it escape, you pesky boy!" shouted Goblin-Gaius at Merlin. "Go after it. Shoo! Shoo!" Merlin left the room and Goblin-Gaius knelt down by the treasure chest. He started to lick the gold coins.

Later that day, Merlin returned the apothecary to find it in complete chaos. "It's that pesky goblin!" shouted Goblin-Gaius. "I'm going to the tavern." Merlin couldn't believe his ears; Gaius never went to the tavern!

At the tavern, an arm-wrestling contest was in full swing. Goblin-Gaius noticed that the winner was paid in gold coins. His tongue snaked out of his mouth and he drooled. All that gold! The unlikely old man soon beat the champion and gathered up the gold – the goblin's magic was strong.

The next morning, Morgana came to see Gaius. Her healing bracelet that helped her sleep had gone missing and she needed a sleeping potion to help her. Goblin-Gaius gave her a bottle with some purple liquid in it. On his way back from the market, he then called in at Gwen's house and convinced her that there was a plague sweeping Camelot. He forced her to take a remedy from him, in exchange for some gold, of course.

Goblin-Gaius made up a vial of the purple liquid to treat Uther's baldness and, after making him drink some of it, applied it to his head and then smacked him. Whack! "Is it really necessary to slap my head like that?" asked Uther. Goblin-Gaius assured him it was, to encourage the circulation and make Uther's hair grow back.

Back at his quarters, Goblin-Gaius put his gold into the chest and licked it lovingly. Unknown to him, Merlin was watching. "You're the goblin!" he cried. He demanded that the goblin leave Gaius but the goblin refused because of the fun he was having. "It's a bit old and creaky, but ever so much fun!" he said.

In the quiet court, as Arthur warned of random acts of vandalism and theft around the castle, a loud farting noise seemed to escape from Gwen, who looked deeply embarrassed for being so unladylike. As everyone stared aghast, Morgana made a similar noise and then Uther farted loudly and furiously, too! The court was quickly dismissed and Goblin-Gaius couldn't stop smirking.

Merlin had started to worry that the goblin was going to get Gaius into trouble. When Goblin-Gaius said he was going to the tavern, Merlin magically locked the door and told him he couldn't. Goblin-Gaius realized Merlin had magical powers and threw a dagger at him. Merlin reversed it and sent it back to Gaius, but stopped short of harming him. "That's your problem!" remarked Goblin-Gaius, "I can hurt you, but you can't hurt me without hurting Gaius!"

Merlin decided to find Arthur and ask for his help. But as he entered the corridor, he was arrested and dragged before Uther, who accused him of being responsible for all the embarrassing afflictions that the court had lately been suffering from. Goblin-Gaius had produced a spell book with evidence of Merlin's sorcery.

Merlin retaliated with the accusation that Gaius has been possessed by a goblin, but naturally Uther wouldn't listen to him and Merlin was sentenced to death. As he was dragged away to the cells, Merlin tried to make Arthur see sense, but a sad Arthur knew there was nothing he could do to help his friend without proof.

That night, Goblin-Gaius visited the tavern and was very rude to Sir Leon. He spat ale into his face and forced Sir Leon to draw his sword on him. At the last minute he apologized and ordered a flagon of ale for the knights. But not before he had sneakily added a potion to it!

Merlin escaped from his prison using a touch of magic and fled to Gwen's house. Once she had recovered from the shock of such news, they discussed how to get the goblin out of Gaius. Merlin was convinced that he could find the answer in Gaius's books, if he could get to the apothecary ...

Arthur thanked Goblin-Gaius for his help in exposing Merlin. Goblin-Gaius said that he was pleased to help and that he was looking forward to seeing Merlin hang. But Arthur knew that Gaius would never wish Merlin dead. Arthur now knew that Merlin had been telling the truth all along. Goblin-Gaius realized he was about to be exposed and, using a spell to displace a nearby vase, swiftly knocked Arthur out.

Gwen was going to see Arthur to tell him that Merlin was telling the truth and that Gaius had been possessed by a goblin, when she heard a honking sound. As she entered Arthur's chambers, she found him sitting on the floor. He had long, grey donkey ears and when she talked to him she realised he could only bray like a donkey!

Back at the apothecary, Merlin had found a way to make the goblin leave Gaius, but it was a big risk. Gwen was alarmed when she found out. "You want to kill Gaius?" she asked.

"Just until the goblin leaves," said Merlin. He had carefully made a poison and also an antidote, which he asked Gwen to be on hand to administer as soon as the goblin left Gaius.

Sir Leon was looking for Gaius because his face was covered in boils! He begged Goblin-Gaius for a remedy and Goblin-Gaius demanded payment in gold as usual. As Goblin-Gaius left Sir Leon and made his way back to the apothecary, Gwen and Merlin got ready. Merlin poured the poison all over the gold coins and Gwen had the antidote.

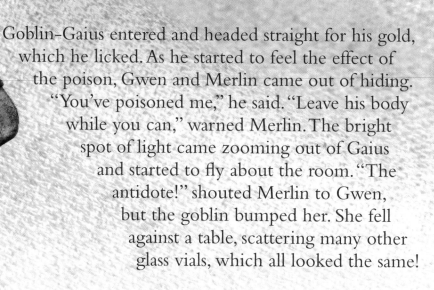

Goblin-Gaius entered and headed straight for his gold, which he licked. As he started to feel the effect of the poison, Gwen and Merlin came out of hiding. "You've poisoned me," he said. "Leave his body while you can," warned Merlin. The bright spot of light came zooming out of Gaius and started to fly about the room. "The antidote!" shouted Merlin to Gwen, but the goblin bumped her. She fell against a table, scattering many other glass vials, which all looked the same!

Merlin tried to catch the goblin, as it zoomed all around the room, looking for an escape. It suddenly made for Merlin's mouth and dived in. Merlin leapt for the lead lined box, spat the goblin in and slammed the lid closed. He quickly locked it and then leapt up to help Gwen.

As they scrabbled among the bottles, it became clear that unless they could find the antidote quickly, Gaius would die. Merlin chose one bottle and then threw it away. He picked another and then rushed to administer it to Gaius. "Are you sure that's the antidote?" asked Gwen.
"No!" said Merlin, but tried it anyway.
"Come on, Gaius, you stubborn old goat!"

After a terrible moment that seemed to go on forever, Gaius whispered, "Who are you calling a stubborn old goat?" He was saved!

At last everything was made clear to Uther and the court and Gaius stated Merlin's innocence. Uther ordered that the goblin should be placed in the vaults of the castle. "Do you know who was responsible for releasing the goblin in the first place?" Uther asked Gaius. Merlin shifted nervously.
"I'm afraid I have no idea, my lord," replied Gaius.

Merlin and Gaius took a stroll about the castle and discussed the events of the goblin and how Merlin had reversed the spells. They passed Prince Arthur, winning a practice fight. He laughed, but his laugh turned into a braying sound and he looked worried.
"Merlin!" Gaius said.
"Just one more day!" said Merlin, grinning.

GOLD TRAP

Merlin and Gaius have laid a trap to catch the goblin.
Can you spot all the gold before he does?
There are nine pieces to find!

GOBLIN CURSE

Help Merlin find a cure for the people affected by the goblin's curse. Unscramble the letters and set them free!

Gaius has been invaded by a

b o n i g l

g o b l i n

Uther has lost all his hair and is

d a l b

b a _ _ d

Arthur has got the ears and voice of a

n e d y o k

d o n k e y

The knights have got these on their faces

l b i o s

_ _ _ _ _

MERLIN SUDOKU!

Solve the puzzle below by making sure that
each column and row has one of each
character in it. Each box must have
one of each in it too! Good luck!

HOW TO INSULT YOUR FUTURE KING

Merlin has devised a code where he can insult Arthur when he's frustrating him and Arthur won't know a thing. Use the key to rearrange the letters to find the insults. There are some clues to help you!

KEY

A	B	C	D	E	F	G	H	I	J	K	L	M
U	V	W		Y	Z	A				E	F	

N	O	P	Q	R	S	T	U	V	W	X	Y	Z
I	J	K		M			P	Q				

1

O	S	H	K	I	O	R	K
l		m		e		l	e

2

I	R	U	Z	V	U	R	K
				p			

3

J	U	R	R	U	V	N	K	G	J
			p		e				

4

Y	Z	G	X	Z	R	K	J

Y	Z	U	G	Z

5

Z	U	G	J

21

ARE YOU READY TO BE A KNIGHT OF CAMELOT?

What type of Knight of Camelot are you?

Q1. No-one can fail to notice Gwen and Arthur's blossoming romance. Are you . . .

A. Happy that your friends are happy, but too busy having fun to settle down.

B. Pleased. Gwen's not of noble birth, but she acts like a gentlewoman and is a good choice for Arthur.

C. Hiding your heartbreak, but you would never get in the way of your future King's happiness.

Q2. You're out for a ride when you pass through a village and spy a tavern you haven't yet sampled. Do you . . .

A. Jump straight off your horse and head over for several tankards of mead.

B. Decide that it looks a little rough and make for your local tavern in Camelot instead.

C. Hesitate but you'll have one drink – you love meeting new people.

Q3. Merlin is Prince Arthur's servant and regularly joins in to help protect the King and Camelot. What is your opinion of him?

A. He's the closest thing you have to a friend and you value him dearly.

B. He obviously does his job well and Prince Arthur seems to like him.

C. He has saved Prince Arthur again and again and you know his big secret. You consider him a very special and brave friend.

Q4. Every knight has a different way of life: some knights travel together, some wish to fight their battles alone. Do you . . .

A. Travel alone and don't really make close friends. Life is much simpler that way.

B. Travel with your band of trusted knights – you couldn't imagine life without them.

C. Make friends wherever you go and enjoy the company of others, but also like being on your own.

Q5. What's your stand on the use of magic?

A. You think that sometimes it can be useful but you prefer using physical strength to win battles.

B. Magic is forbidden in Camelot so it is your responsibility to report anyone using it.

C. You are wary: one of your friends uses magic for good, but you know it can also be used for great evil.

Q6. Arthur asks who is willing to fight alongside him. Do you volunteer?

A. Slim odds and a small chance of survival, you wouldn't miss it for the world!

B. You've fought alongside Arthur many times, you can't think of anyone you'd rather die for.

C. Of course, Arthur has been good to you and taught you the knightly code – you owe him your protection.

Q7. The Knights of Camelot live by the knightly code. Are you . . .

A. Not particularly bothered: you live by your sword and try to do good but you don't have time for rules.

B. Proud to live by the knightly code. You always have done, and chivalry is natural to you.

C. Not of noble birth but you would give anything to be a knight and live your life strictly by the code.

Q8. Gwen has helped you to escape from the dungeon. But she gives you a dress as a disguise. Is it worth the shame?

A. Why not? You'll try anything, as long as you can take your sword. It'll be a hilarious story to tell in the tavern later.

B. If there was any other option you'd take it, wearing a dress is the most embarrassing thing you've ever done, but you put it on in good faith.

C. You'd do anything for Guinevere.

Q9. It's the day of the tournament, are you competing?

A. Of course! You're raring to go, you love a challenge.

B. You're ready to do your duty and protect Prince Arthur if it looks like he's in danger.

C. You know you shouldn't, it's knights only, but you can't resist and a little white lie won't hurt . . .

Q10. Morgana demands your allegiance and asks you to betray Arthur. Do you . . .

A. Feel flattered by the attentions of such a lady . . . but you would never betray your friends.

B. Shout 'Long live the King!' and tell her you'd rather die than hurt Arthur.

C. Tell her that your allegiance lies completely with Arthur, and inform him of her betrayal.

MOSTLY A's

You're very much like Gwaine. You live by your sword and your own rules. You're the kind of person that has fun wherever you go, and although some may find it difficult to see past your jokes, they're just a defence mechanism. In reality you are very fond of your friends and can always be relied on to protect them in a fight.

MOSTLY B's

You're an original Knight of Camelot, just like Sir Leon. You'd lay down your life for Arthur and for Camelot because first and foremost in your mind is your duty to your King and his people. You are mature, responsible and people look to you to lead them in times of trouble, as you are often wise beyond your years.

MOSTLY C's

You've wanted to be a knight all of your life just like Lancelot. You live by the knightly code and have legendary courage as well as gentleness. After years of feeling spare, you finally feel like you belong. You've never been happier, although your love for a certain Guinevere causes you pain, as you know that she loves another.

THE CRYSTAL CAVE

Merlin and Arthur had been running for ages but they just couldn't seem to lose the crowd of bandits that were fast on their heels. As they turned a corner Arthur beckoned Merlin on. "Trust me," he said. Merlin stopped and gulped. The gigantic statues and the very atmosphere of the place that Arthur was keen to hide in seemed to be telling him to turn back.

"What is this place?" Merlin asked nervously.
"It's the valley of the fallen kings," replied Arthur.
"They'll never follow us into here, they'll be too scared."
But then they heard the bandits still hard on their heels.
They started running again.

The twang of an arrow flew through the air. Arthur fell to the ground. He'd been hit! Merlin dragged him to safety and hid in the bushes. He looked down at Arthur. He was breathing but not conscious. Merlin started to insult him to see if Arthur would react. "Come on, dollophead," he murmured. "I need you to recover. You Royal imbecile!" But it was no use, Arthur's eyes remained firmly shut and his face grew whiter.

Merlin used all the magic he knew over Arthur's wound but, he couldn't heal it. He went to the pool nearby to wash his hands. They were wet with the blood from Arthur's wound. He started to weep, had he saved Arthur's life all those times before for him to die now?

"Tell me, why are you so sad?" A voice asked him. He looked up and an old man was standing in front of him.

"Because my friend is dying," Merlin replied. "And I can't help him."

"The time for him to die is not yet upon him," replied the old man. "I am Taliesin." He moved over to Arthur and uttered a deep magic spell and turned Arthur over. Arthur breathed easier and colour returned to his cheeks. Merlin couldn't believe his eyes. The old man beckoned him to follow . . .

"I want to show you something, Merlin," said Taliesin and he led him into a cave. "This is where magic began, it is the Crystal Cave." Merlin walked into the cave, it was full of the most beautiful crystals, hanging from the ceiling and dripping from the walls. As Merlin walked further into the cave he began to see images in the crystals, a woman – it looked like Morgana – was sitting on Uther's throne as Queen. He backed away.

Taliesin beckoned him back. "They contain futures that are not yet born. Use what you see for good." As Merlin watched, a horse reared and an ornate dagger was unsheathed. Morgana in a red cloak was walking along a corridor in the dead of night. Red liquid dripped from a finger. Fire blazed and finally he saw Morgana with a dagger standing over Uther . . . Merlin cried out and clutched his head.

Merlin rushed back to Arthur, he knew they had to get back to Camelot as fast as possible. Arthur was standing up and completely cured. "You look like a startled stoat, Merlin," he commented. Merlin couldn't speak; his mind was whirling with what he had seen. They started back for Camelot.

They arrived back in time for Morgana's birthday banquet. Uther was most concerned to hear of the bandits who had attacked them on their own land. Later that day, Merlin had a chance to share what had happened with Gaius. "Taliesin died about three hundred years ago, he was a great seer to kings and it is rumored he used the Crystal Cave for his prophecies," Gaius commented. "But there is nothing to suggest that what you saw is imminent, is there, Merlin?" Merlin shook his head.

The next day Arthur informed Merlin that he needed to get a birthday present for Morgana and after much deliberation he settled on a dagger as her gift! Merlin wasn't so sure. As Merlin hurried back to Gaius he saw Morgana struggling with a rearing horse, exactly as he'd seen in the crystals. Merlin was stunned; the vision appeared to be turning into a reality.

Arthur proudly showed the dagger he'd chosen for Morgana to Merlin. It was quite plain and not at all like the one he'd seen. Maybe the vision wouldn't come true after all. He breathed a sigh of relief and poked fun at Arthur for buying Morgana such a plain present. Didn't women normally like pretty things, like jewellery?

Later that evening Morgana's birthday banquet was in full swing. Merlin looked on as Morgana unwrapped her gift from Arthur. She held it up in front of her and was silhouetted against the moonlight. Merlin was shot through with fear – the knife was beautifully jewel-encrusted as in the second vision from the cave.

Arthur turned and smiled at the young warlock – he was right, girls do like pretty things. Merlin couldn't believe what was happening, his actions appeared to have realised his fears.

Merlin decided that he would have to watch Morgana day and night to stop the vision he'd seen from reaching its terrible finale. Merlin sat concealed in a nook outside Morgana's room. He was determined not to let her out of his sight. As she prepared for bed he saw her breathe on a mirror she'd been given for her birthday. A secret message appeared. It was from Morgause. It read, 'Sister, come to the darkling wood at midnight.'

Morgana left her room and strode down the corridor in a red cloak, exactly like Merlin's vision. He paced after her, frantically thinking what to do and how to stop her. As she came past some stairs and to a set of doors, he magically closed them in front of her and knocked a flaming lamp down on her. As she tried to shield herself, she fell down the stairs. She lay still and Merlin ran for Gaius.

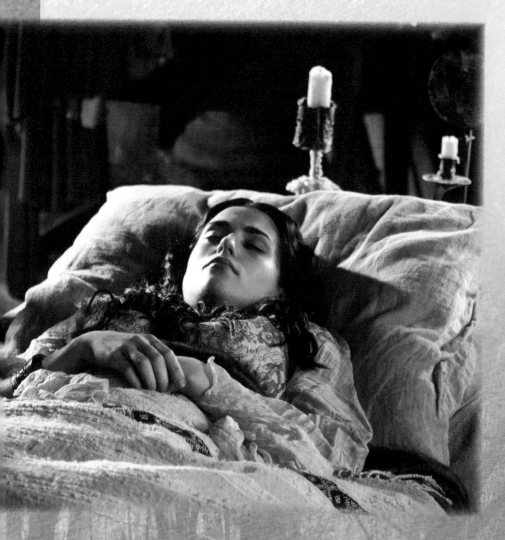

Gaius had Morgana carried to his chambers but there was not much he could do. He stitched the wound on her head but part of her skull was broken and she was bleeding to death. Merlin was devastated. "I had to stop the future, I had to stop Morgana killing Uther . . . I wish there could have been some other way," he said to Gaius.

Uther and Arthur were crushed by Morgana's fatal state. Arthur told Merlin, "I've grown up with her, she's like a sister to me. I'd sacrifice my place on the throne for her to see another sunrise." Merlin was consumed with guilt. He returned to Morgana just in time to hear Uther reveal that Morgana was his daughter to Gaius. Uther asked Gaius to do anything he could to save her, even using the old religion . . . that meant magic!

Morgana's condition grew worse. Gaius told Gwen that her breath was leaving her body and that she couldn't last until morning. Gwen wept over Morgana. Merlin had decided that he had to do something. He had never intended for this to happen and he knew he was the only one who could stop it.

He left the castle at nightfall and set out on his own. Once he came to a clearing, he stopped and summoned the Great Dragon. When the dragon came, Merlin explained what had happened and asked him to help in saving Morgana. "Merlin, have you learnt nothing?" asked the Great Dragon. "I am a dragonlord, you cannot refuse me!" shouted Merlin. "I command you." "The evil that will follow is of your doing, and yours alone," said the Great Dragon to Merlin. He breathed his fire over Merlin and turned to fly away.

Merlin raced back to Camelot and with all the power he could muster, he uttered the Great Dragon's incantation over the unconscious Morgana. Almost instantly, she started to stir. The dragon's spell had cured her.

Uther was overjoyed that Morgana had recovered. "You mean everything to me," he said to her. Morgana replied that Uther was like a father to her and she now realized how important Arthur and Uther were.

She added, "but none of the people know. In their eyes, I'm just your ward."

"What matters is what we feel . . . not what the people think," said Uther. Morgana looked upset.

That night, as Camelot slept, a cloaked figure slipped into the citadel: it was Morgause. The sorceress found her way to Morgana, dispatching a hapless servant on route. Morgana was cold, emotionless. She had news for her sister – she's Uther's daughter. Morgause was stunned but delighted by the news. This meant Morgana had a legitimate claim to the throne. Morgana, on the other hand, only wanted vengeance on the father who had disowned her. By saving the Princess's life, Merlin had put the King in danger once again.

Merlin and Gaius found the dead servant. He'd dropped a decanter of red wine. Gaius ran his fingers through it and it dripped from his finger. Merlin recoiled in horror, it was another image from the crystals!

He hadn't managed to stop the future after all. He knew that Morgana would act quickly.

Merlin ran to Morgana's chambers and tried to stop her from leaving. He told her that Arthur had sent him to watch over her, but she overpowered him with her own magic. The sudden woosh caused the candles nearby to flare and the curtains caught alight. Merlin was left alone, unconscious in her chamber as flames licked around him.

When Merlin woke he saw fire, the fifth image from the crystals. He ran to Uther's chamber. Morgana was about to stab Uther with her ornate dagger. Merlin muttered a spell and the window exploded, waking Uther. He was surprised to see Morgana. Thinking as quickly as she could, she told the King that she was scared of the fire and just wanted to be near him. Merlin looked on, aghast, as Uther took her into his arms.

"You saved the King's life," said Gaius to Merlin.
"I thought I could alter the future but instead I caused it, I made it happen," said Merlin. Gaius nodded wisely.
"I fear that Morgana knows the truth . . . she knows that the King is her father," Gaius said. "And that means that Arthur is all that stands between her and the throne of Camelot."

MERLIN'S VISION

Merlin is led into the Crystal Cave by the wise seer, Taliesin, and sees the future. Can you spot the one difference between the vision in the crystals?

A

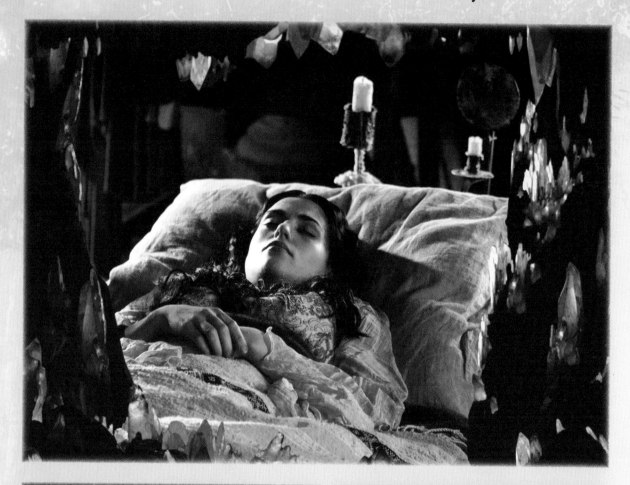

B

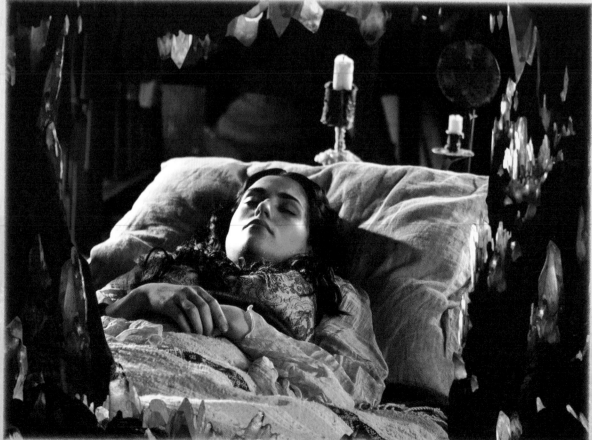

MIRROR MESSAGE

Morgause has managed to smuggle a secret
gift to Morgana. Hold this page up to a mirror
and the message will reveal itself.

GAIUS

This wise physician is Merlin's counsel and friend. Being the only person at court who knows about Merlin's powers, he offers advice and covers for Merlin. As dark forces grow, and Camelot's hour of need has come closer, he has once or twice started to use magic again, but only in situations where he can see no other way. Ever loyal to Uther and Arthur, he has become distrustful of Morgana.

UTHER

Uther is a strong king who has ruled for many years, commanding respect through fear and banning the practice of magic. But his rule looks to be nearing the end. Arthur is proving himself to be a worthy successor to the throne and Uther is deeply proud of his son. But when Uther is finally dethroned by Morgana, his heart is broken. That his daughter, who he has cherished all these years, should turn on him is the ultimate betrayal.

THE GREAT DRAGON

The Great Dragon, Kilgarrah, no longer dwells beneath Camelot after being freed by Merlin. But Merlin is still able to call on him because he is a dragon-lord and Kilgarrah cannot refuse him. When he asks him to help Morgana, the dragon cannot understand why Merlin wants to save her, and warns him that as a result of his action great evil will follow.

GWAINE

A silver-tongued, likeable rogue who is superb with a sword. Gwaine could be a knight, being of noble birth, but he prefers to live the life of a lone wolf. Although he's still banned from Camelot by Uther, he finds himself helping Merlin and Arthur on many occasions. Named 'Strength' by the Fisher King's gatekeeper, Grettir, Gwaine saves both Merlin and Arthur from death by wyverns.

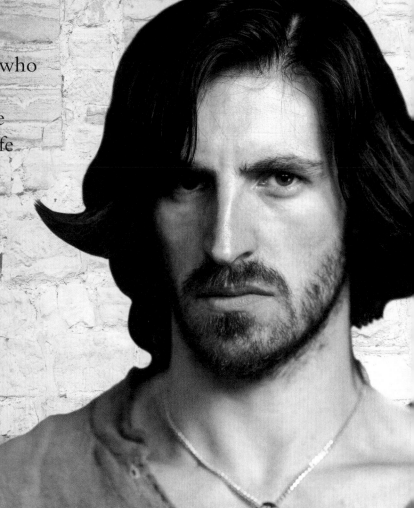

THE EYE OF THE PHOENIX

The quest Arthur had chosen was a dangerous one. He would venture to the Perilous Lands and retrieve the Golden Trident from the Fisher King, as told in the legends of the fallen kings. "To prove yourself worthy of the throne you must complete this task, alone and unaided," Uther told Arthur. Arthur nodded, he was eager to start his quest and he hurried to make preparations for his departure.

At dinner, Merlin and Gaius spoke of Arthur's choice of quest. Gaius told him that the Fisher King was a sorcerer many hundred years ago. The legend was that he was wounded in battle and his wound festered. The infection spread not just through his body but his lands as well, turning them into wasteland. They were not called the Perilous Lands for no reason. Gaius added that some believed the Fisher King was still alive, kept from death by his magic.

In the lower town, while Morgana and Gwen were shopping, an old crone caught Morgana's arm and begged for a word. Morgana turned to look at the old woman and saw her sister, Morgause, staring at her. She quickly led her to a quiet place. "This disguise will not hold for long, sister," said Morgause. "What quest has Arthur chosen?" She smiled as Morgana revealed that Arthur was to find the trident of the Fisher King and visit the Perilous Lands.

"Take this and give it to Arthur as a token of your good wishes before he sets out on his quest," Morgause handed Morgana a bracelet with a strange golden stone set into it. "When the time is right, make an image of Arthur and bind it as I showed you." Morgana nodded. "When he does not return, you, sister, will take your rightful place as sole heir to the throne of Camelot," Morgause continued. She hurried away.

All of Camelot gathered to see Prince Arthur set out on his quest. As Morgana turned to Uther, she saw he was frowning. "You look troubled, sire," she commented.

"He is sole heir to the throne, Morgana," replied Uther.

"Don't worry, I'm certain that a Pendragon will rule over Camelot for a long time to come," Morgana said, with a strange smile.

Merlin helped Arthur up into his saddle. He was drawn to the power emitted from the enchanting stone that the prince was wearing as a bracelet. Arthur noticed him looking at it. "A present from Morgana," he said. Merlin frowned but said nothing.

As soon as Athur had left Camelot, Merlin raced back to find Gaius and ask him if he knew what the stone in the bracelet could be. He suspected the gift from Morgana could be highly dangerous.

They searched every book they could find for the stone but none of them matched. Merlin was getting desperate; he had to find out what Morgana had given Arthur. "We've examined every stone imaginable," said Gaius.
"Unless . . . " He walked over to a shelf and pulled off a dusty old tomb. "Was this it?" He showed an exact copy of the stone. Merlin nodded excitedly. "This is no stone," said Gaius. "It's the Eye of the Phoenix. Some call it the fire bird and it will burn and consume the life force of anybody who comes into contact with it."

Secretly in her chamber, Morgana made the image of Arthur and bound it as Morgause had shown her. She then set it on fire with a spell of dark magic. Far away where Arthur was sleeping for the night, the bracelet started to glow, the Eye was working!

With Arthur in danger, Merlin knew that he had to go to him, even though the prince had made it clear that he wasn't to have any assistance. Merlin needed someone else to help him and the only person he could think of was Gwaine. He wasn't the easiest man to track down, but he knew a good place to start. Merlin started to search the taverns in Engerd, a nearby village. He came across a brawl in one of them and in the centre of the tumult was . . . Gwaine. A quick exit was needed!

Meanwhile, Arthur had arrived at the edge of the Perilous Lands and slowed as he approached a bridge. A small man by the name of Grettir appeared. "You must be Courage," he said. "You'll need Strength and Magic if you are to succeed in your quest." Arthur frowned.
"I don't condone the use of magic," he said.
"The rules in the land you're heading to are quite different to the world you know," replied Grettir wisely.

"That's a very beautiful bracelet," commented Grettir.
"It was a gift from someone very dear to me. She hoped it would bring me good fortune," replied Arthur.
"Did she now?" said Grettir. "How very thoughtful of her." He cackled and Arthur started to walk over the bridge. He glanced back. Grettir had disappeared!

Gwen was feeling uneasy about Morgana's recent secretive behaviour. Her room had an odd smell, and she was sure the old crone that Morgana had helped in the lower town wasn't all she seemed. Whilst cleaning her mistress's chambers, Gwen noticed a silver box and she started to investigate. Footsteps approached and the maidservant quickly hid. From her hiding place she watched Morgana use some sort of dark magic and the contents of the box burst into flames.

At the same time, much further away, Arthur was crossing the Perilous Lands. As Morgana cast her spell, the Eye of the Phoenix started to glow and he felt the energy draining from him. The prince stumbled, fell into a swamp and started to sink. The swamp was sucking him in! Just as he started to go under, he managed to use his sword to lever himself to freedom. He hauled himself out and lay gasping on dry land.

Finally, Merlin and Gwaine came to the bridge of the Perilous Lands, where Arthur had been not too long ago. Grettir appeared once more. "So Magic has arrived," he said to Merlin. "Your presence is essential so that Arthur can succeed." Gwaine followed quickly behind. "And finally Strength has arrived, so the trio is complete." Grettir smiled.
"Who are you?" asked Merlin.
"I am the keeper of the bridge," replied Grettir. "I only wish to see the Fisher King's lands restored and prosperity reign again. The Fisher King has waited many years for this day, do not deny him what he wishes."

At nightfall, Merlin and Gwaine made a fire and sat quietly talking. Suddenly, an unearthly noise ripped through the night.
"What's that?" Merlin said.
"A pheasant," replied Gwaine.
"A pheasant?" repeated Merlin.
"A very big one!" said Gwaine.

The next day, Arthur approached a tall, ominous-looking tower with some creatures circling above it – the Fisher King's castle. When the flying wyvern saw him approaching they started to attack. With the little energy he had left, he managed to fend them off with his sword and get into the castle. The Eye on the bracelet was glowing brightly. Arthur swayed and stumbled as he made his way through the castle. Merlin and Gwaine weren't far away.

"I don't think they're pheasants," said Merlin, as they looked at the circling creatures.
"No, they're wyvern," replied Gwaine. "Distant cousins of dragons."

They approached the castle and entered. But Arthur was nowhere to be seen and the wyvern had also disappeared.

They split up and searched the castle. At the top of a flight of stairs in a little room, Merlin found Arthur seemingly unconscious and about to be

devoured by two wyvern. He used magic to drive them away and rushed to Arthur's side. He pulled the Eye of the Phoenix bracelet off Arthur's wrist and Arthur instantly woke. He was not pleased to see Merlin or Gwaine. "You've completely ruined my quest!" he complained.

"There are more wyvern on the way, we'd better get out of here," said Gwaine but Arthur was determined to get the trident before they left. Up the stairs the trio found a throne room. It was dusty, full of cobwebs and decay. Merlin stepped in and a secret trap released the door.
He was trapped inside! Arthur and Gwaine called to him but he couldn't hear them.

Merlin turned to look round the room and saw a throne with an old, old man sitting on it.
"So, Emyrs, you're here at last," he said.
"So you are still alive," breathed Merlin.
"For now," said the Fisher King.

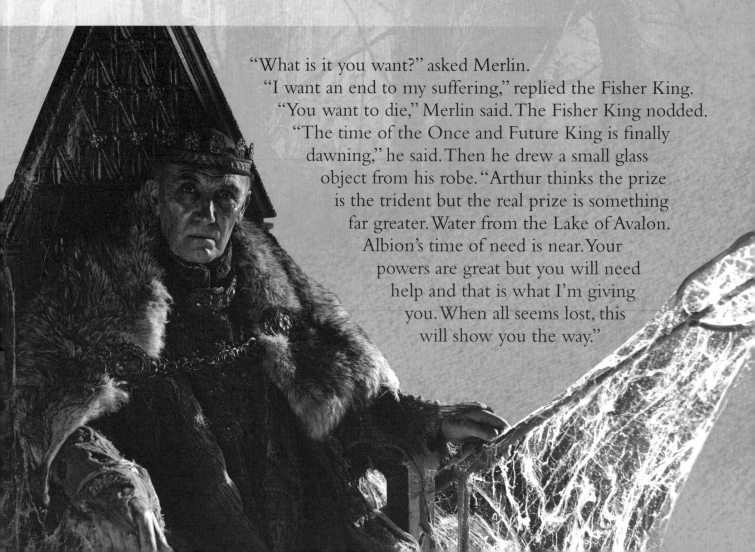

"What is it you want?" asked Merlin.
"I want an end to my suffering," replied the Fisher King.
"You want to die," Merlin said. The Fisher King nodded.
"The time of the Once and Future King is finally dawning," he said. Then he drew a small glass object from his robe. "Arthur thinks the prize is the trident but the real prize is something far greater. Water from the Lake of Avalon. Albion's time of need is near. Your powers are great but you will need help and that is what I'm giving you. When all seems lost, this will show you the way."

Merlin took the water.

"I've given you a gift. Now you must give me one in return," said the Fisher King.

"I have nothing to give," said Merlin, but then he remembered the bracelet. The Fisher King held out his arm and Merlin placed the bracelet on it. Almost immediately a wind started to blow and the Fisher King disappeared. Finally, Gwaine and Arthur manage to break through the door. Merlin looked at them, unable to tell them all he had just experienced.

Arthur strode over to the throne and chuckled with glee, the trident lay on the floor. He grabbed it and held it aloft.

At Camelot's border they stopped to say goodbye to Gwaine. He was still banned from Camelot by Uther. "I'll remember this, Gwaine," Arthur said. Gwaine nodded and started to ride off. "You were not there. You haven't seen me for days," said Arthur to Merlin, as they started to ride towards the castle.

Out of her chamber window Morgana was shocked to see Arthur riding back into the castle. Her bracelet hadn't done its work. Uther was delighted to see his son back. He had proved himself and would one day make a fine king.

FISHER KING WORDSEARCH

Look carefully at this wordsearch square and see if you can find all the story words and characters listed. The words read up, down, backwards, forwards and diagonally.

T	M	S	P	Q	U	E	S	T	W	K	I	N	G
E	O	X	H	O	R	S	E	R	D	P	G	E	H
T	R	W	O	E	R	I	F	R	U	Z	R	G	I
N	G	S	E	P	S	H	O	M	K	H	E	D	E
E	A	A	N	R	G	W	E	N	E	L	T	I	S
D	N	B	I	W	S	Y	A	T	G	L	T	R	U
I	A	U	X	U	O	V	T	M	C	J	I	B	A
R	O	C	K	S	S	E	G	I	P	I	R	N	G
T	U	T	H	E	R	R	N	L	D	C	G	P	R
V	A	V	A	L	O	N	E	R	E	Y	E	A	O
M	E	R	L	I	S	T	R	E	N	G	T	H	M
C	O	U	R	A	G	E	T	M	E	R	L	I	N
P	E	R	I	L	O	U	S	L	A	N	D	S	X
X	I	N	E	N	I	A	W	G	W	A	N	T	O

ARTHUR	GRETTIR	MERLIN	STRENGTH
AVALON	GWAINE	MORGANA	SWAMP
BRIDGE	GWEN	MORGAUSE	SWORD
COURAGE	HORSE	PERILOUS	TOWER
EYE	KING	PHOENIX	TRIDENT
FIRE	LANDS	QUEST	UTHER
GAIUS	MAGIC	ROCKS	WYVERN

MAGIC BRACELET

Merlin is about to give the Eye of the Phoenix
bracelet to the Fisher King. Before he does,
can you help him spot the odd one out?

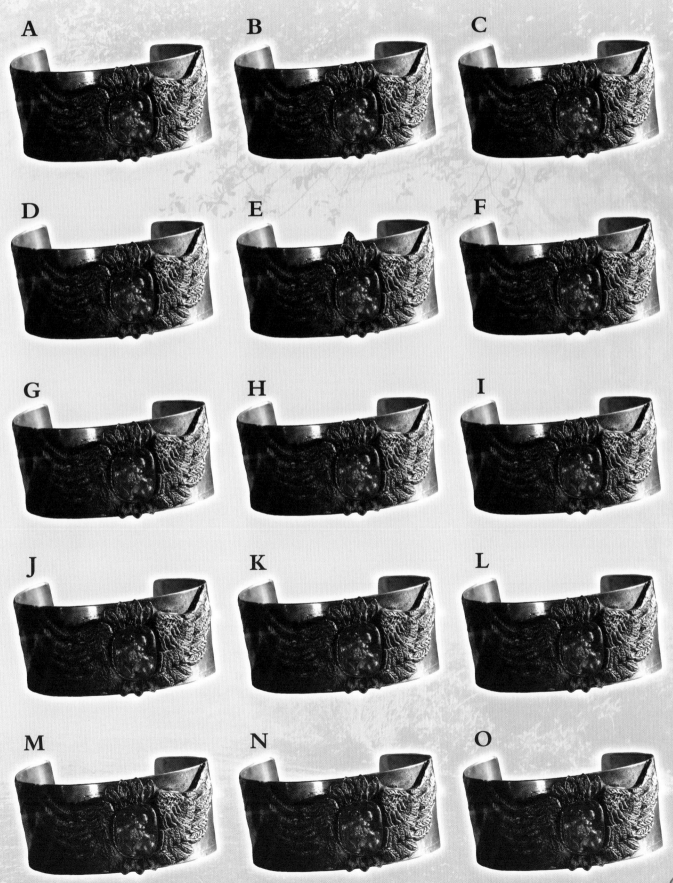

A B C

D E F

G H I

J K L

M N O

MORGANA'S SPELLS

Morgana has become very accomplished in the dark arts. Use the key to work out what evil spells she has inflicted on other people.

1.

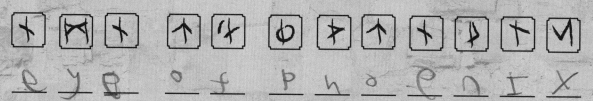

e y e _ o f _ p h o e n i x

This, when worn in a bracelet by Arthur, starts to drain his life force. It is given by Merlin to the Fisher King to help him leave this world.

2.

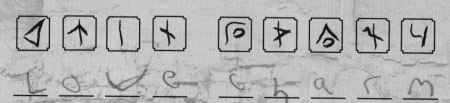

l o v e _ c h a r m

Morgana has a dreadful vision that Gwen is going to be queen. She decides to act and uses this to denounce Gwen as a witch.

3.

m a n d r a k e

Morgana collects Uther's tears and uses them for this spell. She then places it under Uther's bed. It slowly turns him mad.

KEY

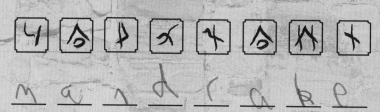

A	B	C	D	E	F	G	H	I	J	K	L	M

N	O	P	Q	R	S	T	U	V	W	X	Y	Z

MORGAUSE

This powerful sorceress uses dark magic and evil spells to forward her wicked ambitions. She only wants one thing – her sister on the throne of Camelot – and she is determined to see King Uther dethroned and Prince Arthur killed to achieve that aim. Cenred has proved to be a useful ally and his army a great help in her plans so far, but they are only a means to an end . . .

GRUNNHILDA

As Princess Elena's maid since her birth, Grunnhilda has always been by her side and is her most trusted companion. But Grunnhilda has a secret, she is a pixie and in thrall to the Sidhe who rule her. When her mistress was a baby, Grunnhilda helped the Sidhe, and Elena has had one living inside her for most of her life. Grunnhilda's mission is to help Elena marry Prince Arthur, so at last a Sidhe can reign at Camelot.

CENRED

Cenred's land borders Camelot and he has coveted the kingdom for as long as he can remember. He will stop at nothing to achieve his aim. Morgause is invaluable to him, feeding him information and helping him set traps for Prince Arthur. When the Cup of Life is found and an immortal army has been created, Morgause decides that he has outlived his usefulness.

THE COMING OF ARTHUR

The Cup of Life had been discovered among the druid people. The druids had used its powers to cure Sir Leon when he was on the verge of certain death. The lucky knight returned to Camelot and told King Uther and Prince Arthur of his fortune and the existence of the mystical object. Determined that Cenred should not get the cup, Uther ordered Arthur to find it and bring it back to Camelot to keep it safely locked away. Although Merlin and Arthur used all their efforts to retrieve the cup, it fell into Cenred's hands and Morgause used it to create an immortal army . . . Camelot was about to face its biggest threat.

Under attack from the most powerful army imaginable, Camelot swiftly fell and Uther was dethroned and put in the dungeon. With Arthur injured and in hiding, Morgana took her place as Queen and revealed to Uther that she knew he was her father. Arthur, Merlin and Gaius, among others, had managed to escape Camelot and evade capture but it was only a matter of time before their hiding place in the forest would be discovered. They needed a plan, but Arthur was not himself. Merlin had been busy thinking of what they could do, he'd even sent a secret message for Lancelot.

Morgana was finding her new role of queen more difficult than she had expected. The knights of Camelot would not pledge allegiance to her. She put them in the main square and had the archers take aim at them. Believing they were about to die, Sir Leon and his fellow knights started to shout, "Long live the King!" But Morgana, from her place on the royal balcony, lifted her arm and directed the archers to fire on innocent civilians instead. It was a lesson for the knights that she intended them not to forget.

Arthur had not moved for days. He was stunned by Morgana's betrayal. Merlin offered him some dinner but he waved it away. Merlin was spurred on to try and make him see sense. "I understand your father lied to you about Morgana . . . but he's still your father, he needs you. Camelot needs you."

"I've known her all my life, how could she do this to us?" Arthur replied. Merlin didn't know what to say. Arthur added, "We can't defeat an immortal army." Merlin grinned. "We don't know, until we try," he said. Arthur took the food Merlin had offered and started to eat.

Morgana was worried that without the knights pledging their allegiance, the people of Camelot would not yield. Gwen offered to go and talk to Sir Leon to try and make him see sense. When Gwen was ushered into the cell by a guard and told Sir Leon that she was supposed to be asking him to bow to Morgana, he tried to throw her out. But then she told him that what she was actually going to do was rescue him so they could join Prince Arthur. Morgana and Morgause, unseen, watched Gwen talk to Sir Leon. It was obvious that she was going to betray them.

Merlin spoke to Gaius, who explained that the only way the immortal army could be defeated was for the Cup of Life to be emptied, but that involved getting close enough to the cup in the first place. Merlin was perplexed: how would they manage such a task?

Merlin decided that the time had come to use the water from the Lake of Avalon that the Fisher King had given him. He broke the glass and the water flowed over a rock, creating a pool. Freya appeared in the reflection. She said, "I swore that one day I would repay you and now is the moment. There is but one weapon that can slay something that is already dead. That weapon lies at the bottom of the Lake of Avalon." Merlin was overjoyed to see her but didn't understand how the sword, Excalibur, would slay the immortal army.

"The immortal army are living men," he replied. "The moment they entered their pact with Morgause they became the living dead," replied Freya and vanished, her message was complete.

Merlin secretly left the cave and summoned the Great Dragon, Kilgarrah, to take him to the Lake of Avalon. The dragon carried him there and reminded him that in the wrong hands, the sword would do great damage. He told the young warlock that when Camelot was safe once more, the sword must be placed where no mortal man can wield it. Merlin rowed onto the lake and the sword came up attached to a hand. He reached out and took it.

With the help of Gwen, and disguised as a women courtier, Sir Leon broke out of his cell and together they escaped into the forest. Morgause wasn't fooled by the disguise and took some of the immortal army and followed them. They managed to reach Arthur and his men, but Morgause and her army were hot on their trail.

Luckily, Elyan spotted the ambush and raised the alarm just in time. They set off. Merlin ran to get Gaius, who was afraid he would slow them down. But Merlin disagreed – he knew that Camelot needed both of them. Gaius started after the others and Merlin snatched up Excalibur. Now he was ready for the immortal army!

As Merlin made his way to Arthur and the others, he realized that the army stood in the way of Arthur and the path out of the cave. The great rocks above them suddenly started to fall, creating a barrier and cutting the army off. They looked up to see Lancelot and his friend Percival. Merlin's message to Lancelot had been delivered. They'd arrived just in time and managed to save them!

Arthur led his men and Gwen up to a high castle. It had belonged to the ancient kings many years ago. Arthur uncovered a round table and asked everyone to join him in sitting at it. He began, "This table was used by the ancient kings of Camelot. A round table afforded no man or woman more importance than any other . . . It seems fitting that we revive the tradition now."

Arthur continued, "For too long my father has languished in prison. Tomorrow I make my bid to rescue him. Are there any round this table who will join me?" Lancelot stood. "You taught me the code of knights, justice, freedom and all that's good."

Elyan followed. "Even though I was a commoner, you were willing to lay down your life for me." Sir Leon stood. "I have fought alongside you. There is no-one I would rather die for." Gwaine then rose. "I think we've no chance but I wouldn't miss it for the world." One by one, they all stood and supported Arthur until there was just Merlin left sitting at the table. Arthur sighed. "Merlin?" he growled. "No, I don't really fancy it," replied Merlin, grinning. "You don't have a choice, Merlin," said Arthur.

Arthur beckoned them all to follow him. "I'm going to do something my father wouldn't approve of," he said. He asked Lancelot, Gwaine, Elyan and Percival to kneel. He touched each man on the shoulder with his sword and knighted them. Gwen, Merlin and Gaius looked on with approval.

As they tried to get some rest before the start of the battle, Lancelot asked Merlin what he was planning. He knew that Merlin would have some kind of idea. "Morgana has the Cup of Life. If I can find it and empty it, she will lose her power," whispered Merlin. "Aren't you forgetting something? It's guarded by an immortal army," frowned Lancelot. "Aren't *you* forgetting something? I have magic!" replied Merlin.

The next day they made preparation to leave. Arthur instructed Gwen to stay behind with Gaius. "There will be casualties," he said. "Gather firewood and make bandages." He continued, "I want you to know if I never see you again . . . " he stopped. "You will see me," replied Gwen gently. "I watched you last night, you gave us hope . . . I saw the king you will become."

They left and made their way to the castle. Merlin and Lancelot started to try and find the Cup of Life. When they were surprised by an immortal solider, Merlin used Excalibur to kill him. Lancelot was stunned by the sight of such an impressive sword and the soldier seeming to blow into nothing. "It was forged in the dragon's breath" Merlin explained.

Merlin and Lancelot managed to fight past more soldiers to get into the room where the Cup of Life was. As they locked the door behind them, they turned to the Cup of Life. More soldiers were guarding it!

The rest of the knights found themselves outnumbered in the cells. Arthur managed to throw some cell keys to the other imprisoned knights and they quickly poured out of the cells to join the fight. Arthur stole away to rescue his father. He found a broken man in Uther, but was adamant there was no time for emotion . . .

The fight became desperate. More and more immortal soldiers started to appear and Arthur could see that it was hopeless. He cried out, "If we're going to go down, we'll go down fighting. For the love of Camelot!" The cheer was taken up by all the men.

As Merlin managed to fight off the last soldier, he turned and ran for the Cup of Life but he wasn't in time. The doors opened and Morgause appeared. She magically lifted Merlin up and threw him against the wall. "I've got a feeling I won't be seeing you again," Morgause said to him.

A voice behind her said, "No, you won't," and Gaius strode in and used all his ability to conjure a powerful spell. He lifted her and she fell against the wall, hitting it with such force that her neck seemed to break. She lay still. Merlin emptied the Cup of Life with Excalibur. The immortal army was no more! In the midst of the fighting, the soldiers suddenly disappeared. Arthur and his men couldn't believe their eyes.

When Morgana saw Morgause lying on the floor, she started to scream and ran to her. "It's over, Morgana," said Merlin. "You're wrong, this has just begun," she replied and started to howl. Her grief shattered the windows and the room started to crumble.

The battle for Camelot was over and the Prince had been victorious, but the King was a broken man. "Perhaps we're heading for a new time, you may need to take charge and become King," Merlin said to Arthur. Arthur nodded but his attention was suddenly caught by the sight of Gwen, escorted back to Camelot by his knights. He went to her and they kissed in full view of everyone.

There was no sign of Morgana or Morgause. They had disappeared. A search was made but no-one could find them. There was only one thing left to do. Merlin took Excalibur into the woods and plunged it into a stone, where no-one could take it . . .

EXCALIBUR!

Look at the picture clues. Write each character's name in the right row on the grid and something will be revealed.

HIDDEN BEASTS

The magical creatures which have threatened
Camelot are hidden on this page.

The letters
in the shaded
boxes spell
out something
that can defeat
them all!

5 letters	– sidhe, troll, afanc, pixie
6 letters	– goblin
7 letters	– griffin, serkets
8 letters	– skeleton
9 letters	– gargoyles, manticore
10 letters	– cockatrice, wilddeoren
12 letters	– immortal army
13 letters	– questing beast

ALBION ADVENTURE

Start at number one and choose which path
you want to take. Create your own adventure!

1 In the castle of Fjirien on the sea of Meridor, you are in the labyrinth under the castle. You come to a fork in the path, do you take the left turn (jump to 2) or the right turn (jump to 3)?

2 You escaped the labyrinth, but on your way back to Camelot you come upon some of Cenred's men in the valley of the Fallen Kings. You run for your life, do you head up along the top ridge of the valley (jump to 4) or keep low (jump to 5)?

8 Camelot is being over-run and there is not much time to escape. Do you try to find Arthur and the others in a cave you know of (jump to 10) or go to the Castle of the Ancient Kings, because they'll get there at some point (jump to 11).

7 The Forest of Ascetir is inhabited by druids. Cenred's men force you to get the Cup of Life for them. Once they have it, you manage to escape. Do you head for Camelot (jump to 8) or wander through the forest until you come to a lake (jump to 9)?

9 At the Lake of Avalon, a hand holds out a sword. It's Excalibur! Do you take it straight to Merlin in the cave (jump to 10) or take it straight to the stone that you saw it sticking out of in the Crystal Cave (jump to 13).

10 Arthur, Merlin and the others have left the cave. You think they must have gone to the Castle of the Ancient Kings (jump to 11). Or maybe they are already attacking Camelot (jump to 12).

3 On the way back from the labyrinth you come through the White Mountains, but bandits are waiting for you. You struggle but go along quietly (jump to 6). You yell and attract the attention of some of Cenred's men (jump to 4).

4 You've been brought to Cenred's castle and Cenred and Morgause are discussing what to do with you. You tell them you've found the Cup of Life and they force you to take them to it (jump to 7). You're quiet and say nothing, so they decide to give you to the slave trader, Jarl (jump to 6).

6 Jarl lives in the Forest of Gedney. His slaves are forced to fight one another to the death for his amusement. You manage to break out, but do you retrace your steps to the Valley of the Fallen Kings and end up in the Crystal Cave (jump to 5) or manage to get back to Camelot (jump to 8)?

5 You've escaped Cenred's men and made it to the Crystal Cave. It feels eerie and full of magic. Do you head back to Camelot as fast as you can (jump to 8) or have a closer look into the crystals, where you can see a sword in a lake (jump to 9).

11 At the Castle of the Ancient Kings, the others are overjoyed to see you. You're just in time to help them fight. Do you go with Merlin (jump to 13) or with Arthur (jump to 12).

12 Camelot has been saved and it's all thanks to your fighting. Well done!

13 Excalibur's work is done and you and Merlin can put the sword in the stone together. Good work!

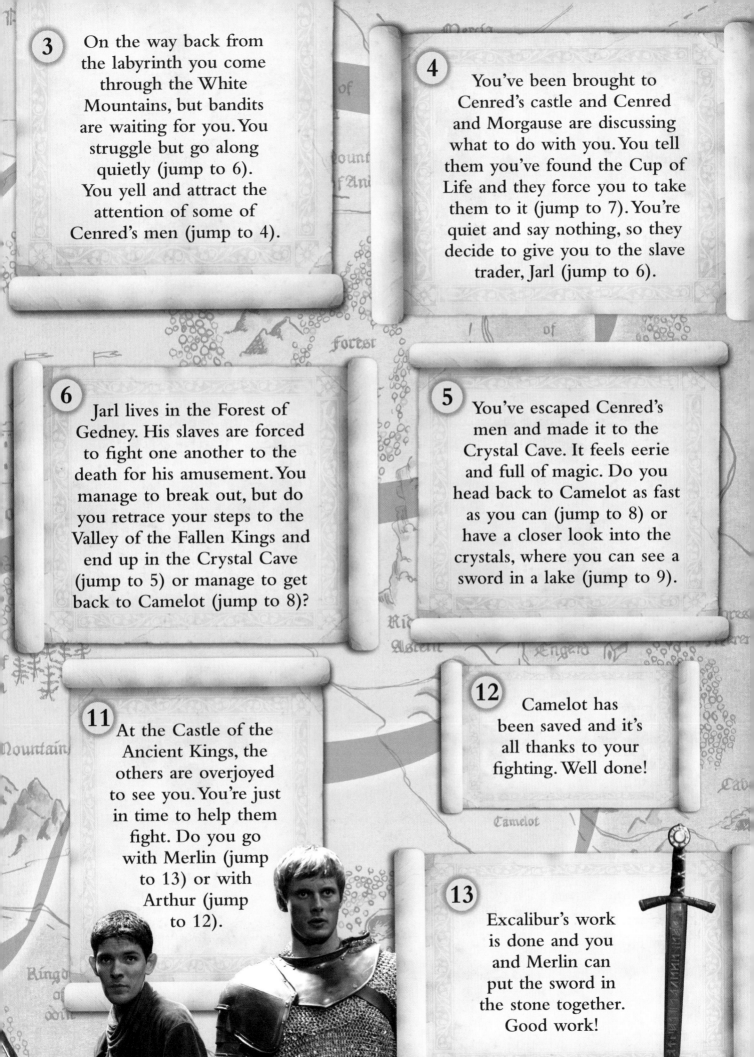

ALICE

Before the Great Purge, Alice worked side by side with Gaius as a skilled healer. Gaius is delighted to see her back in Camelot. He has felt guilty for years after allowing her to leave and never trying to follow. But now Alice is possessed! A manticore is controlling her and she is back in Camelot for one reason only, to kill the King!

ELENA

This princess is not a typical, delicate young lady. But then not every princess was a changeling child. At birth, Elena was taken over by a Sidhe with big ambitions for her future. The Sidhe will stop at nothing to marry her to Prince Arthur and gain the throne of Camelot.

GILLI

The tournament was a test of skill and bravery and anyone was allowed to enter. Yet no-one could quite understand why this young boy was winning as much as he was. Merlin spied the signs of magic and tried to warn Gilli to use his magic for things that mattered, not just personal gain. But Gilli was tired of being downtrodden and weak, magic made him feel powerful and strong!

ANSWERS

Page 8 – Camelot Characters

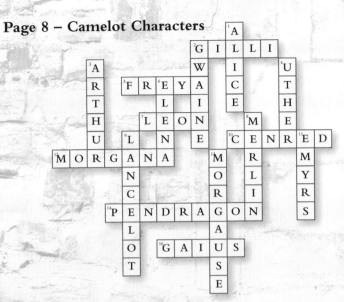

Page 9 – Deadly Disguise!
It's Morgause!

Page 18 – Gold Trap

Page 19 – Goblin Curse
• Gaius has been invaded by a goblin.
• Uther has lost all his hair and is bald.
• Arthur has got the ears and voice of a donkey.
• The knights have got these on their faces – boils.

Page 20 – Merlin Sudoku!

Page 21 – How to Insult your Future King
1. imbecile
2. clotpole
3. dollophead
4. startled stoat
5. toad

Page 32 – Merlin's Vision

Page 33 – Mirror Message
'Sister, come to the darkling wood at midnight.'

Page 44 – Fisher King Wordsearch

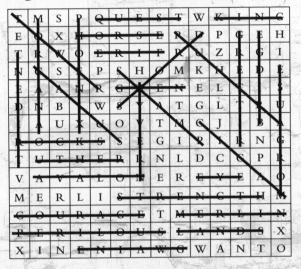

Page 45 – Magic Bracelet
E is the odd one out.

Page 46 – Morgana's Spells
1. Eye of Phoenix, 2. Love charm, 3. Mandrake

Page 56 – Excalibur!
IN THE STONE
1. GAIUS, 2. MERLIN, 3. UTHER, 4. ARTHUR,
5. CENRED, 6. MORGAUSE, 7. LANCELOT,
8. MORGANA, 9. GWAINE, 10. GWEN

Page 57 – Hidden Beasts
EXCALIBUR can defeat them all!

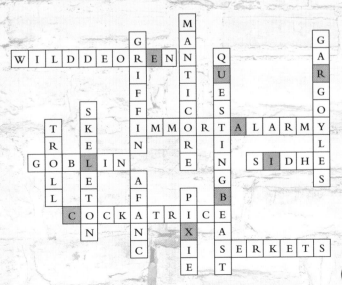